THE GREAT BIBLE
DISCOVERY

THE ACTS OF THE APOSTLES

THE BIBLE IS A BEST-SELLER. IT IS ALSO ONE OF THE MASTER-WORKS OF WORLD LITERATURE - SO IMPORTANT THAT UNIVERSITIES TODAY TEACH 'NON-RELIGIOUS' BIBLE COURSES TO HELP STUDENTS WHO CHOOSE TO STUDY WESTERN LITERATURE.

THE BIBLE POSSESSES AN AMAZING POWER TO FASCINATE YOUNG AND OLD ALIKE.

ONE REASON FOR THIS UNIVERSAL APPEAL IS THAT IT DEALS WITH BASIC HUMAN LONGINGS, EMOTIONS, RELATIONSHIPS. 'ALL THE WORLD IS HERE.' ANOTHER REASON IS THAT SO MUCH OF THE BIBLE CONSISTS OF STORIES. THEY ARE FULL OF MEANING BUT EASY TO REMEMBER.

HERE ARE THOSE STORIES, PRESENTED SIMPLY AND WITH A MINIMUM OF EXPLANATION. WE HAVE LEFT THE TEXT TO SPEAK FOR ITSELF. GIFTED ARTISTS USE THE ACTION-STRIP TECHNIQUE TO BRING THE BIBLE'S DEEP MESSAGE TO READERS OF ALL AGES. THEIR DRAWINGS ARE BASED ON INFORMATION FROM ARCHAEOLOGICAL DISCOVERIES COVERING FIFTEEN CENTURIES.

AN ANCIENT BOOK - PRESENTED FOR THE PEOPLE OF THE SECOND MILLENNIUM. A RELIGIOUS BOOK - PRESENTED FREE FROM THE INTERPRETATION OF ANY PARTICULAR CHURCH. A UNIVERSAL BOOK - PRESENTED IN A FORM THAT ALL MAY ENJOY.

M publishing
CARLISLE, UK

23

Acts tells the fascinating story of how the good news about Jesus spread from Jersualem in Asia to Rome in Europe, the capital of the Roman Empire. Some people think this amazing book should be called 'The Acts of the Holy Spirit' It features two apostles in particular.

Peter, who had known Jesus during his earthly life, took the lead at first, working in Jerusalem and the neighbouring towns, telling Jews about Jesus. He also took a revolutionary step when, guided by the Holy Spirit, he visited and baptized the centurion Cornelius, a Gentile.

The other apostle was originally named Saul - after the first Hebrew king. Because he belonged to a family which had the privilege of Roman citizenship, he had another name - Paul. Although he grew up outside Palestine, he studied in Jerusalem and became a rabbi. He persecuted those who claimed that Jesus was the messiah. But Jesus appeared to him and called him to be an apostle.

At first the Christians could not believe that their enemy had become their friend. Paul spent several years quietly rethinking his beliefs and studying the Old Testament from his new viewpoint. Later he travelled through the cities of what we now call Turkey and Greece, proclaiming the good news. Here he spoke to Gentiles - people whom other Jews regarded as second class. These non-Jews worshipped many deities, their beliefs were a mixture of superstition and Greek philosophy, their standards of sexual morality were low.

While he was with them Paul gave the young churches he founded the teaching and practical advice they so greatly needed. After leaving them, he wrote letters confirming and developing what he had already said to them and advising on fresh questions. These letters are still read today all over the world.

When Paul finally reached Rome, it was through an event which seemed like a disaster. His Jewish enemies saw to it that he was arrested in Jerusalem. For over two years he was a prisoner of the Roman governor. But God used these happenings to bring Paul to the capital of the empire, where he was able to preach freely for two years to the believers, to Jews and to pagans.

ACTS OF THE APOSTLES 9-20

23

THE ACTS OF THE APOSTLES

First published as *Découvrir la Bible* 1983

First edition © Larousse S.A. 1984
24-volume series adaptation by Mike Jacklin © Knowledge Unlimited 1994
This edition © OM Publishing 1995

01 00 99 98 97 96 95   7 6 5 4 3 2 1

OM Publishing is an imprint of Send the Light Ltd.,
P.O. Box 300, Carlisle, Cumbria CA3 0QS, U.K.

Introductions: Peter Cousins

British Library Cataloguing in Publication Data
A catalogue record for this book is available from the British Library
ISBN 1-85078-227-x

Printed in Singapore by Tien Wah Press (Pte) Ltd.

THE FIRST PERSECUTION AGAINST JESUS' FOLLOWERS CLAIMED MANY VICTIMS.
THOSE WHO MANAGED TO ESCAPE, WENT ON SPREADING THE GOOD NEWS.
THE SANHEDRIN APPOINTED SAUL, WHO HAD AGREED TO STEPHEN'S MURDER, TO DIRECT THE PERSECUTIONS.

THERE! JERUSALEM HAS BEEN RID OF THE NAZARENES...

YES, SAUL, BUT THE RINGLEADERS HAVE ESCAPED! YOU MUST HUNT THEM DOWN!

DO YOU KNOW WHERE THEY'RE HIDING?

YES, CAIAPHAS. IN JOPPA AND SAMARIA AND ANTIOCH, BUT ESPECIALLY IN DAMASCUS.

PETER AND PAUL
THE GOOD NEWS IS TOLD TO THE PAGANS

THEY'VE BEEN PREACHING THEIR MESSAGE IN MANY SYNAGOGUES...

FROM TOMORROW, SAUL, YOU'LL HAVE FULL AUTHORITY TO ARREST THEM AND BRING THEM HERE FOR TRIAL.

CAIAPHAS, DO YOU THINK WE'LL BE ABLE TO CONTROL THE SITUATION?

I HOPE SO. AT ANY RATE, SAUL IS THE MAN WE NEED!

SCENARIO: Etienne DAHLER
DRAWING: Carlo MARCELLO

3

SAUL AND HIS ESCORT IMMEDIATELY LEFT JERUSALEM FOR DAMASCUS.

AFTER A DIFFICULT JOURNEY OF SEVERAL DAYS...

...THE LITTLE GROUP STOPPED TO REST BEFORE REACHING DAMASCUS.

THAT NIGHT SAUL COULDN'T SLEEP.

WE'LL RIDE ON AGAIN TONIGHT. I WANT TO GET TO DAMASCUS AS EARLY AS POSSIBLE.

IF SAUL GIVES THEM AS HARD A TIME AS HE GIVES US, THERE'LL SOON BE NO MORE NAZARENES!

WITH A MAN LIKE THAT THERE'S NO HOPE OF TAKING THINGS EASY!

I'LL BREAK THAT NAZARENE SECT!

SETTING OFF LONG BEFORE SUNRISE, THE RIDERS SOON SAW THE CITY.

DAMASCUS!

LET'S GO!

DURING THAT TIME PETER BEGAN VISITING THE OTHER CONGREGATIONS IN THAT AREA. HE WAS AT LYDDA...

WE'VE COME FROM JOPPA.* TABITHA HAS JUST DIED...

YOU KNOW HOW MUCH SHE DID, AND HOW EVERYONE LOOKED UP TO HER...

VERY WELL! I'LL GO WITH YOU, AND WE'LL PRAY FOR HER.

* Now called JAFFA.

AT JOPPA, IN THE UPPER ROOM WHERE THE DEAD WOMAN LAY...

LOOK AT HER LOVELY WORK... HOW SAD IT IS!

EVERYONE LEAVE THE ROOM!

PETER STAYED ALONE, AND AFTER PRAYING FOR A LONG TIME...

TABITHA! GET UP!

THEN TABITHA OPENED HER EYES, AND SAT UP...

THE WHOLE TOWN HEARD THE NEWS, AND MANY BELIEVED IN THE LORD.

PETER STAYED ON AT JOPPA, WITH A MAN CALLED SIMON. ONE MIDDAY, WHILE HE WAS PRAYING...

PETER! GET UP! KILL AND EAT!

NEVER, LORD! I'VE NEVER EATEN ANYTHING FORBIDDEN OR UNCLEAN.

WHAT GOD SAYS IS CLEAN YOU MUSTN'T CALL UNCLEAN!

PETER WAS STILL WONDERING WHAT THIS VISION COULD MEAN...

HEY! SIMON LIVES HERE, DOESN'T HE?

WE'RE LOOKING FOR SOMEBODY CALLED PETER...

I'M PETER. WHAT DO YOU WANT?

PETER WAS STILL SPEAKING, WHEN THE HOLY SPIRIT CAME DOWN ON ALL THOSE WHO WERE LISTENING.

PETER!
EVEN THE PAGANS RECEIVE THE HOLY SPIRIT!

SO LET US NOT SET A LIMIT TO GOD'S WORK ANY LONGER... LET THEM ALL BE BAPTIZED!

BACK IN JERUSALEM SOME OF THE BELIEVERS CRITICIZED PETER.

IS IT TRUE? YOU ATE WITH PAGANS?

IT IS TRUE. I EVEN PRAYED WITH THEM AND BAPTIZED THEM.

PETER STAYED IN CAESAREA FOR A FEW DAYS, THEN HE SET OFF BACK TO JERUSALEM.

THESE WORDS WHICH THE LORD SPOKE WERE ALSO FULFILLED AT CAESAREA:
'JOHN BAPTIZED WITH WATER, BUT YOU'LL BE BAPTIZED WITH THE HOLY SPIRIT.'

AND TO CALM THEM DOWN, PETER HAD TO EXPLAIN HOW THE LORD HAD LED HIM TO DO THESE THINGS.

They chose Barnabas, who came from Cyprus.

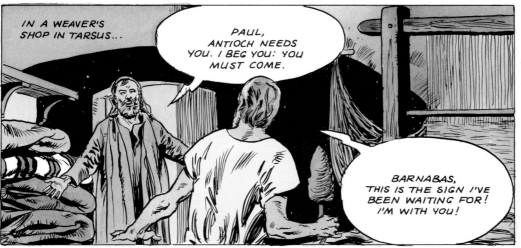

IN A WEAVER'S SHOP IN TARSUS...

PAUL, ANTIOCH NEEDS YOU. I BEG YOU: YOU MUST COME.

BARNABAS, THIS IS THE SIGN I'VE BEEN WAITING FOR! I'M WITH YOU!

ON THE WAY BARNABAS TOLD PAUL THE WONDERFUL THINGS THE LORD HAD BEEN DOING IN ANTIOCH. AT LAST THEY ARRIVED...

THERE, PAUL! THERE IS ANTIOCH!

MAY GOD HELP US TO MAKE HIS CHURCH STRONG.

PAUL'S POWERFUL PREACHING HELPED MANY PEOPLE TO BELIEVE, AND THE CHRISTIANS REGULARLY MET TOGETHER FOR THE AGAPĒ.*

SO, PAUL, HERE YOU ARE AT LAST! WHAT A BLESSING!

EVER SINCE BARNABAS LEFT WE HAVE BEEN PRAYING THAT YOU WOULD AGREE TO JOIN US.

WHAT ARE YOU THINKING ABOUT, PAUL?

WE'VE NEVER MET BEFORE, AND WE'RE ALREADY BROTHERS!

AND THE LORD WILL GIVE YOU MANY MORE!

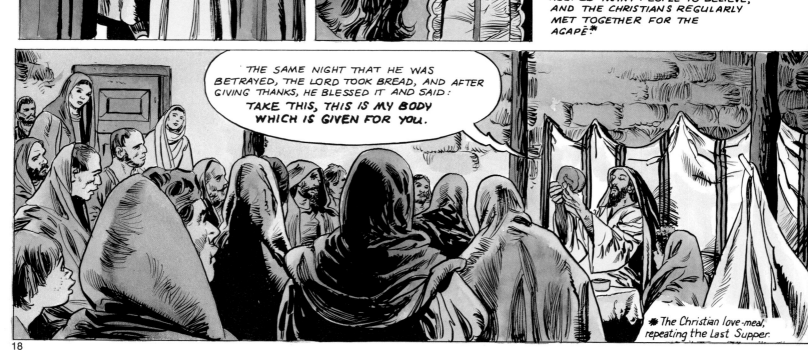

THE SAME NIGHT THAT HE WAS BETRAYED, THE LORD TOOK BREAD, AND AFTER GIVING THANKS, HE BLESSED IT AND SAID: TAKE THIS, THIS IS MY BODY WHICH IS GIVEN FOR YOU.

* The Christian love-meal, repeating the Last Supper.

PAUL HAD BEEN IN ANTIOCH FOR A YEAR, WHEN ONE NIGHT, DURING A MEETING...

THIS IS WHAT THE LORD SAYS: A GREAT FAMINE* IS COMING; IT WILL RAVAGE JUDAEA, AND YOUR BROTHERS WILL LOSE EVERYTHING.

THAT IS AGABUS, A PROPHET FROM JERUSALEM...

WE MUST LISTEN TO HIM. LET'S START COLLECTING MONEY RIGHT NOW TO HELP OUR BROTHERS.

WITHIN A FEW MONTHS THE FAMINE HAD BECOME VERY SEVERE...

PAUL AND BARNABAS, WE'VE DECIDED THAT YOU TWO SHOULD TAKE WHAT WE'VE COLLECTED TO JERUSALEM.

RIGHT YOU ARE!

*This famine broke out between AD 46 and 48, during the reign of the Emperor Claudius.

IN SPITE OF THE FAMINE, I'LL BE GLAD TO SEE JERUSALEM AGAIN!

BUT WHAT IS WAITING FOR US THERE?

A LITTLE LATER THE TRAVELLERS LEFT FOR SELEUCIA, WHERE THEY TOOK SHIP FOR JOPPA.

IN JERUSALEM, KING HEROD AGRIPPA I, WHO HAD BEEN MADE KING SEVERAL YEARS BEFORE BY THE EMPEROR CLAUDIUS, WANTED TO GAIN THE SUPPORT OF THE PIOUS JEWS.

THEY DEMAND THE HEADS OF SOME OF THE NAZARENES! LET IT BE DONE!

THEY'VE ARRESTED JAMES, JOHN'S BROTHER!

A FEW HOURS LATER HE WAS BEHEADED.

SOON AFTERWARDS, PETER WAS ALSO ARRESTED.

PUT A STRONG GUARD ON THAT ONE! I'LL TRY HIS CASE AFTER PASSOVER.

BUT THE NIGHT BEFORE PETER WAS TO APPEAR BEFORE HEROD...

PETER, GET UP!

PUT ON YOUR SANDALS, PICK UP YOUR CLOAK, AND FOLLOW ME!

THE LORD SENT HIS ANGEL TO RELEASE ME FROM HEROD'S CLUTCHES...

THEN PETER RAN TO THE HOUSE OF MARY, MARK'S MOTHER. MANY BELIEVERS HAD GATHERED THERE TO PRAY, WHEN SUDDENLY...

SOMEBODY IS KNOCKING AT THE DOOR!

I'LL GO!

IT IS I, PETER! OPEN QUICKLY!

THAT IS PETER! I KNOW HIS VOICE!

YOU'RE MAD!

MARK, GO AND SEE

PETER!

GOD BE PRAISED!

PETER TOLD THEM HOW HE HAD JUST BEEN SET FREE. HE HAD SOMETHING TO EAT. THEN...

NOW YOU MUST GO!

JAMES,* I ENTRUST THE CONGREGATION IN JERUSALEM TO YOU. MAY THE LORD PROVIDE EVERYTHING YOU NEED.

*James, the brother of Jesus, the leader of the Church in Jerusalem.

A FEW DAYS LATER, PAUL AND BARNABAS REACHED JERUSALEM, AND JAMES WELCOMED THEM.

COME INSIDE, BROTHERS. I'VE IMPORTANT THINGS TO TELL YOU.

PAUL
PAUL'S JOURNEYS

WELL, PAUL, TONIGHT OUR JOURNEY WILL BE FINISHED!

BUT NOT OUR ADVENTURE, BARNABAS... WE'LL HAVE TO TELL THE BROTHERS EVERYTHING!

THE CHRISTIANS IN ANTIOCH HAD SENT PAUL AND BARNABAS ON A MISSION. AFTER BEING AWAY FOR FOUR YEARS, THEY WERE ON THEIR WAY HOME.

SCENARIO: Etienne DAHLER
DRAWING: Victor de la FUENTE

AFTER MEETING THE CONGREGATION, PAUL AND BARNABAS WERE NOT ALLOWED TO REST... EVERYONE WANTED TO HEAR THEIR STORY. SO BARNABAS TOLD THEM...

AFTER WE HAD PARTED FROM JOHN MARK AT PERGA, WE SET OFF FOR ANTIOCH IN PISIDIA.

THERE WE FOUND WORK WITH A JEWISH WEAVER, AND ON THE SABBATH PAUL PREACHED THE GOOD NEWS IN THE SYNAGOGUE...

SO UNDERSTAND THIS, MY BROTHERS: WHEN GOD RAISED JESUS TO LIFE AGAIN, HE FULFILLED FOR US THE PROMISE HE HAD MADE TO OUR FATHERS.

PAUL'S WORDS WERE SO ASTONISHING THAT THE NEXT SABBATH THE SYNAGOGUE WAS FULL TO OVERFLOWING.

THEN SOME OF THE JEWS BECAME VERY ANGRY AND TRIED TO STOP PAUL.

YOU'RE TRYING TO MAKE US LEAVE THE FAITH OF OUR FATHERS! IT'S THE DEVIL SPEAKING!

I HAD TO SPEAK GOD'S WORD TO YOU FIRST...

...BUT SINCE YOU REJECT IT, WE'LL TURN TO THE PAGANS!

PAUL, YOU'LL PAY FOR THAT INSULT!

AFTER THAT WE WERE ABLE TO CONTINUE OUR MISSION AMONG THE PEOPLE WHO WEREN'T JEWS FOR SEVERAL MONTHS... MANY WERE WON FOR CHRIST.

STIRRED UP BY MESSENGERS FROM ANTIOCH IN PISIDIA, THE JEWS STONED PAUL AND LEFT HIM FOR DEAD.

WELL?

HE IS STILL BREATHING...

TAKE HIM TO MY HOUSE!

THE NEXT DAY, AT FIRST LIGHT...

TIMOTHY, LOOK AFTER THIS LITTLE GROUP OF CHRISTIANS...

I'LL DO MY BEST, PAUL.

LET'S GO ON TO DERBE!

THERE PAUL SLOWLY GOT BETTER. ONCE HE WAS ON HIS FEET AGAIN, HE DECIDED TO GO BACK TO LYSTRA, ICONIUM, AND THEN ANTIOCH IN PISIDIA.

IT IS VERY IMPORTANT TO MAKE SURE THAT THESE LITTLE CONGREGATIONS ARE DOING WELL BEFORE WE LEAVE THEM...

AS BARNABAS HAS TOLD YOU SO WELL... I BELIEVE THAT THROUGH ALL THESE DIFFICULTIES...

...THE LORD HAS HELPED US TO OPEN THE DOOR TO PAGANS, SO THAT THEY TOO CAN BELIEVE IN HIM.

AFTER THIS REPORT A SERIOUS DEBATE BEGAN AMONG THE CHRISTIANS IN ANTIOCH.

I SAY THAT PEOPLE WHO ARE'NT CIRCUMCISED CAN'T BE SAVED!

YOU'RE RIGHT! PERHAPS PAUL AND BARNABAS ARE GOING TOO FAST.

FOR MY PART, I TRUST THEM...

I SUGGEST WE REFER THE MATTER TO THE APOSTLES IN JERUSALEM.

SOON THE TWO MISSIONARIES HAD TO EXPLAIN THEIR VIEWS ON THIS SUBJECT.

BROTHERS, WHAT IS THE SENSE IN ASKING A PAGAN TO BE CIRCUMCISED AFTER HE HAS BEEN BAPTIZED?

SO, PAUL, YOU'RE THROWING OUT THE LAW OF MOSES?

YOU YOURSELF SAID THAT CHRIST DID NOT COME TO DO AWAY WITH THE LAW, BUT TO FULFIL IT!

PAUL, THIS IS A PROBLEM THAT MUST BE SOLVED...

AND WHO IS GOING TO DO IT?

SO PAUL, BARNABAS, AND SEVERAL OTHERS SET OUT FOR THE HOLY CITY.

THEY WENT THROUGH PHOENICIA, THEN SAMARIA, AND AT LAST...

BARNABAS, THE LORD IS GOOD! I DIDN'T THINK I'D SEE JERUSALEM AGAIN SO SOON.

THE APOSTLES WELCOMED THEM WITH OPEN ARMS. THEN THEY WERE ABLE TO POSE THE QUESTION.

PETER, IT IS OBVIOUS: THE LAW OF MOSES MUST BE OBEYED!

WE MUST THINK ABOUT IT VERY CAREFULLY, BEFORE WE COME TO A DICISION.

BROTHERS, WE'RE SAVED BY GRACE, NOT BY CIRCUMCISION! THE PAGANS RECEIVE THE HOLY SPIRIT IN THE SAME WAY AS WE DO. I'VE FOUND THAT OUT MYSELF.

AND PETER BEGAN TO SPEAK...

I THINK WE SHOULD SIMPLY ASK BELIEVERS WHO AREN'T JEWS NOT TO HAVE ANYTHING TO DO WITH IDOLS, NOT TO EAT MEAT WHICH CONTAINS BLOOD, AND NOT TO LIVE IMMORAL LIVES.

EVERYONE AGREED WITH JAMES'S SUGGESTION.

SOON THE MESSENGERS FROM ANTIOCH RETURNED HOME. JUDAS AND SILAS WENT WITH THEM, CARRYING A LETTER TO THE LOCAL CONGREGATION.

GOD PROTECT YOU, PAUL, TRAVELLER FOR CHRIST!

WHEN THEY REACHED ANTIOCH, JUDAS READ THE MESSAGE FROM THE CHURCH IN JERUSALEM.

IT SEEMS RIGHT NOT TO ASK ANY MORE OF YOU THAN THAT YOU DON'T EAT MEAT SACRIFICED TO IDOLS, OR MEAT THAT CONTAINS BLOOD, AND THAT YOU DON'T LIVE IMMORAL LIVES.

I BELIEVE WE'VE TAKEN AN IMPORTANT STEP TODAY.

NOW THE GOOD NEWS CAN BE SPREAD TO THE ENDS OF THE EARTH!

A LITTLE WHILE LATER JUDAS WENT BACK TO JERUSALEM, WHILE SILAS DECIDED TO STAY IN ANTIOCH.

GOODBYE, JUDAS.

I THINK IT IS TIME FOR US TO TAKE TO THE ROAD AGAIN TOO.

WHAT ARE YOU THINKING ABOUT, PAUL?

I'M ANXIOUS ABOUT THE BROTHERS IN THE DIFFERENT PLACES; THEY'RE STILL VERY YOUNG IN THE FAITH.

GOOD! I'LL COME WITH YOU... BUT ONLY IF MARK COMES TOO...

MARK? NO! THAT IS IMPOSSIBLE! HE'LL TURN BACK AGAIN THE FIRST TIME WE FACE A PROBLEM!

THEN, PAUL, I'LL NOT GO WITH YOU EITHER...

PLEASE YOURSELF, BARNABAS! I'M SURE I'VE ONLY TO ASK SILAS AND HE'LL GO WITH ME.

YOU'RE RIGHT, PAUL!

.. WHILE BARNABAS TOOK HIS NEPHEW MARK WITH HIM AND SAILED FOR CYPRUS.

PAUL, I HAVEN'T YET TOLD YOU THAT I'M A ROMAN CITIZEN.

SO AM I! IT IS USEFUL FOR GETTING OUT OF TIGHT CORNERS!

PAUL AND SILAS SET OUT FOR SYRIA AND THEN CILICIA...

TIMOTHY! GOD BE PRAISED!

PAUL! I KNEW YOU WOULD COME BACK!

AFTER TARSUS AND DERBE, THE TWO TRAVELLERS ARRIVED AT LYSTRA.

YOU'LL BE SURPRISED! THE CONGREGATION HAS REALLY GROWN AND BECOME STRONGER IN THE FAITH.

I KNOW YOU'LL HAVE HAD A LOT TO DO WITH IT.

THAT SAME EVENING, IN FRONT OF THE WHOLE CHURCH GATHERED TOGETHER ...

TIMOTHY, MAY THE HOLY SPIRIT GIVE YOU STRENGTH AND AUTHORITY!

PAUL AND SILAS SOON LEFT LYSTRA, TAKING TIMOTHY WITH THEM.

PAUL, WHY DID YOU INSIST THAT TIMOTHY BE CIRCUMCISED BEFORE WE LEFT?

BECAUSE HE IS JEWISH ON HIS MOTHER'S SIDE, AND BECAUSE I DON'T WANT HIM TO HAVE TO REMAIN SILENT WHEN WE PREACH IN THE SYNAGOGUES.

COME BACK QUICKLY, TIMOTHY!

PREVENTED FROM GOING TO EPHESUS, THE APOSTLES TURNED WESTWARDS, AND REACHED TROAS.

IT WAS THERE THAT ONE NIGHT PAUL HAD A VISION...

THE LORD HAS SHOWN US OUR ROAD. LET'S GO WITHOUT DELAY.

COME OVER TO MACEDONIA AND HELP US!

I WOULD LIKE LUKE TO COME WITH US. HE IS A DOCTOR, SO HE CAN KEEP AN EYE ON ME.

IF GOD HELPS ME, PAUL!

EARLY THE NEXT MORNING THE LITTLE GROUP SAILED FOR MACEDONIA.

35

A LITTLE WHILE LATER LYDIA AND ALL HER FAMILY WERE BAPTIZED...

IN THE NAME OF THE FATHER, THE SON, AND THE HOLY SPIRIT...

...AND HER HOME BECAME THE MEETING PLACE FOR THE NEW CHRISTIANS.

UNCLEAN SPIRIT! IN THE NAME OF JESUS, I COMMAND YOU TO COME OUT OF THIS WOMAN!

BUT THIS WAS QUICKLY FOLLOWED BY SOMETHING WHICH TOOK AWAY SOME OF THE SUCCESS OF PAUL'S MISSION TO PHILIPPI...

THESE MEN ARE SERVANTS OF THE MOST HIGH GOD. THEY TELL YOU HOW YOU CAN BE SAVED!

PAUL, DO SOMETHING! SHE HAS BEEN SHOUTING AFTER US FOR TWO DAYS NOW.

WHO IS SHE?

A POOR SLAVE-GIRL WHO FORETELLS THE FUTURE, AND THIS EARNS A LOT OF MONEY FOR HER MASTERS.

COME HERE!

THE YOUNG WOMAN WAS SET FREE, AND FROM THAT MOMENT SHE WAS NO LONGER ABLE TO TELL THE FUTURE... WHICH GREATLY UPSET HER MASTERS.

THOSE MEN WILL PAY ME FOR IT!

A FEW DAYS LATER...

SEIZE THEM!

STATE THE CHARGE!

THESE TWO FOREIGN JEWS ARE TEACHING CUSTOMS THAT WE ROMANS AREN'T ALLOWED TO PRACTISE!

SO THEY'RE DISTURBING THE PEACE OF OUR TOWN...

AND BEFORE THEY REALIZED WHAT WAS HAPPENING TO THEM, PAUL AND SILAS FOUND THEMSELVES IN FRONT OF THE MAGISTRATES OF THE TOWN.

HAVE THEM FLOGGED, AND PUT THEM IN PRISON!

AFTER THEY HAD BEEN SEVERELY WHIPPED, PAUL AND SILAS WERE THROWN INTO PRISON.

SILAS, HOW DO YOU FEEL?

LET'S SING PRAISES TO GOD!

SUDDENLY, DURING THE NIGHT...

THE SHAKING IS SO STRONG... THE DOOR WILL BREAK...

THE LORD IS SETTING US FREE, SILAS!

ALL THE DOORS OF THE PRISON FLEW OPEN, AND THE CHAINS FELL OFF THE PRISONERS...

WE MUST SEE TO THOSE WHO HAVE BEEN HURT... AND IF YOU STAY, YOU MAY BE PARDONED.

NO! DON'T RUN AWAY!

WHEN HE SAW WHAT HAD HAPPENED, THE JAILER WAS IN DESPAIR, AND WAS GOING TO KILL HIMSELF.

STOP! WE'RE ALL STILL HERE!

YOUR GOD LIVES!

LET HIM BE YOUR GOD TOO, BECAUSE HE SAVED YOU FROM DEATH...

AND THAT SAME NIGHT THE JAILER WAS BAPTIZED.

THE NEXT DAY EVERYBODY WAS SET FREE...

PAUL! SILAS! WHAT HAPPENED TO YOU?

NOTHING SURPRISING TO THOSE WHO WALK IN THE FOOTSTEPS OF CHRIST, TIMOTHY!

...AND A LITTLE LATER, LEAVING LUKE AT PHILIPPI, THE THREE MISSIONARIES WENT ON THEIR WAY.

AFTER WALKING FOR SEVERAL DAYS, THE THREE TRAVELLERS ARRIVED IN THESSALONI-CA, THE BIGGEST TOWN IN MACEDONIA.

WHAT IS YOUR PLAN, PAUL?

THE USUAL ONE, TIMOTHY. FIRST, TO MAKE CONTACT WITH THE JEWS, AND TO PREACH IN THE SYNAGOGUE. AFTER THAT... WE'LL SEE.

PAUL'S PREACHING MET WITH SOME SUCCESS...

THIS JESUS I'M TALKING ABOUT IS THE MESSIAH YOU'RE WAITING FOR!

THE ELDERS OF THE SYNAGOGUE TOOK NOTE OF WHAT WAS HAPPENING.

LET'S START A RIOT. THEN WE CAN ACCUSE THESE TRAITORS OF CAUSING IT!

THEY'RE STAYING WITH JASON. WE CAN ARREST THEM WITHOUT ANY DIFFICULTY.

JASON GOT OFF WITH A FINE. THE FOLLOWING NIGHT...

GO TO BEREA. YOU'LL BE SAFE THERE.

PAUL AND SILAS WERE WARNED IN TIME, AND HID. AT JASON'S HOME...

THEY'VE FLED!

THEN THAT IS TOO BAD FOR YOU, JASON! YOU'LL PAY FOR THEM!

THE JEWS IN BEREA WELCOMED PAUL'S WORDS. A FEW MONTHS WENT BY...

PAUL, SOME JEWS FROM THESSALONICA ARRIVED THIS MORNING. THEY'RE STIRRING UP THE LOCAL PEOPLE AGAINST YOU.

THAT IS THE SIGN FOR ME TO LEAVE... SILAS AND TIMOTHY, YOU STAY HERE A LITTLE LONGER... I MUST GO...

WHERE TO, PAUL?

ATHENS!

SOME CHRISTIANS FROM BEREA WENT WITH PAUL. SOON THEY REACHED THE WONDERFUL CITY.

LIKE THE PHILOSOPHERS, PAUL WENT TO THE PUBLIC SQUARE EVERY DAY, TO TEACH HIS DOCTRINE.

... AND SO, ON THE THIRD DAY JESUS LEFT THE TOMB.

IN MANY WAYS A VERY STRANGE PHILOSOPHY!

HE IS FROM THE EAST! BUT SOME OF WHAT HE SAYS IS INTERESTING...

LET'S INVITE HIM TO EXPLAIN HIMSELF BEFORE THE MEETING OF THE AREOPAGUS.*

* A kind of council of wise men. It was this council which had condemned Socrates four centuries earlier.

A LITTLE LATER IN FRONT OF THE AREOPAGUS...

WE WANT TO KNOW WHAT THIS NEW TEACHING MEANS. EXPLAIN YOURSELF...

AS I WAS WALKING THROUGH YOUR CITY, I SAW AN ALTAR DEDICATED TO AN UNKNOWN GOD... WELL, IT IS THIS VERY GOD I'VE COME TO TALK ABOUT...

THEN PAUL GAVE THEM A LONG EXPLANATION OF THE GOD OF ISRAEL AND HIS MESSENGER JESUS.

HOW CAN YOU CLAIM THAT THE BODY MUST BE RAISED? ISN'T IT THE SOUL'S PRISON?

THAT IS ENOUGH! YOU MAY SPEAK TO US AGAIN ABOUT THIS ANOTHER DAY.

IT IS RIDICULOUS!

MANY DIDN'T WANT TO ACCEPT WHAT PAUL SAID, BUT A FEW BELIEVED AND BECAME CHRISTIANS. ONE OF THEM WAS DIONYSIUS, A MEMBER OF THE COUNCIL OF THE AREOPAGUS.

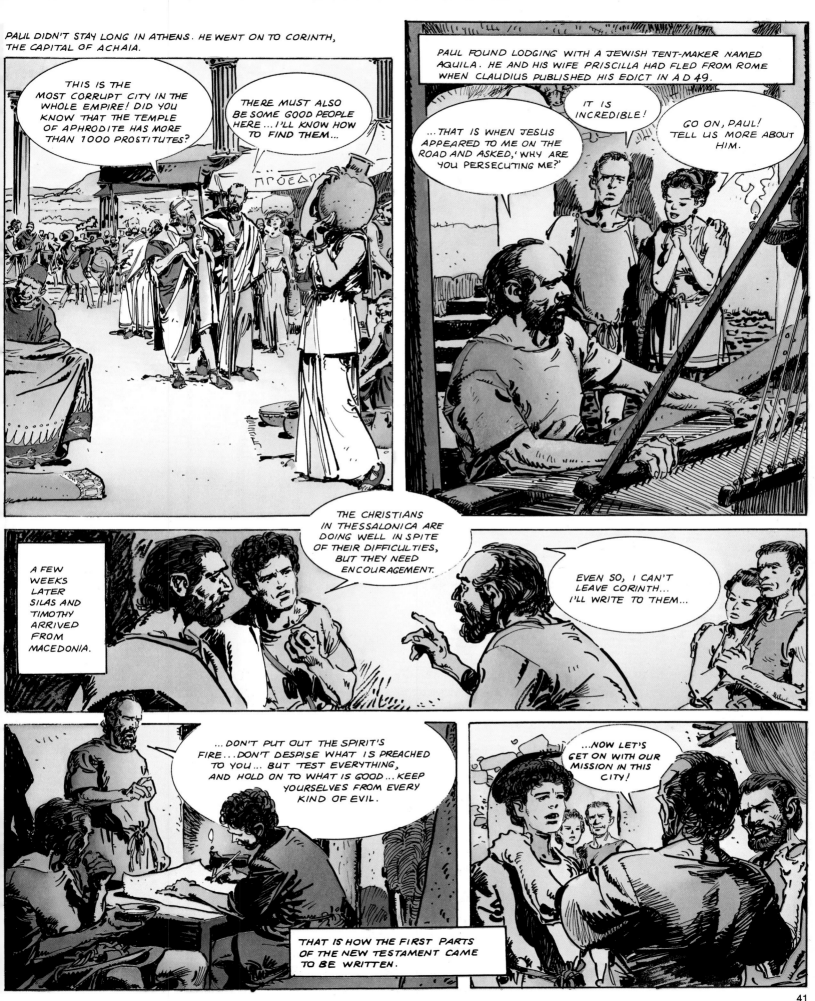

IN CORINTH THE PREACHING OF THE THREE APOSTLES WAS MORE AND MORE SUCCESSFUL. SO THE JEWS BROUGHT PAUL BEFORE GALLIO, THE PROCONSUL.

THIS MAN IS TRYING TO GET THE PEOPLE TO SERVE GOD IN WAYS THAT ARE AGAINST OUR LAW.

THESE ARGUMENTS ABOUT DOCTRINE HAVE NOTHING TO DO WITH ME. I WON'T TRY THIS SORT OF CASE!

THE COURT IS ADJOURNED!

THEN THE ANGRY JEWS TURNED ON SOSTHENES, THE LEADER OF THE SYNAGOGUE...

THIS IS ALL YOUR FAULT! FOR MONTHS YOU ALLOWED HIM TO PREACH IN THE SYNAGOGUE!

YOU TRAITOR! YOU'RE ONE OF THEM!

THEY WERE SO ANGRY THAT THEY BEAT HIM WITH STICKS.

AFTER THAT PAUL STILL STAYED ON IN CORINTH, BRINGING MANY PEOPLE TO BELIEVE IN JESUS CHRIST. THEN IN THE SPRING OF THE YEAR 52...

SO, PAUL, YOU'VE DECIDED TO LEAVE?

I'VE BEEN HERE NEARLY A YEAR AND A HALF. OTHER PEOPLE ARE WAITING FOR ME... AND I'VE MADE A VOW... I MUST BE IN JERUSALEM BEFORE PASSOVER.

AT CENCHREAE, THE PORT OF CORINTH, PAUL SHAVED HIS HEAD, FOLLOWING NAZIRITE* CUSTOM. THEN HE SAILED FOR EPHESUS.

WHO WOULD HAVE THOUGHT THAT THE LORD COULD DO SUCH WONDERFUL THINGS IN A CITY LIKE THIS!

REMEMBER ONE THING, AQUILA: WHERE THERE ARE MANY SINS, THERE IS EVEN MORE GRACE!

* As long as his vow lasted, the Nazirite (a specially dedicated person) didn't cut his hair. When his vow ended, he had to shave his head, then go to the Temple in Jerusalem, to burn his hair on the altar and offer sacrifices.

PAUL DIDN'T STAY LONG IN EPHESUS, WHERE HE LEFT AQUILA AND PRISCILLA. HE HURRIED ON TO JERUSALEM. WHEN HE HAD DONE WHAT THE LAW LAID DOWN ABOUT HIS VOW, HE RETURNED TO ANTIOCH. HE SPENT THE WINTER OF 52-53 THERE, THEN...

WHAT A LOVELY DAY! ...SPRING IS COMING...

THE BEST TIME OF THE YEAR TO TRAVEL...

YOU'RE OFF AGAIN, PAUL?

I MUST GO AND VISIT THE CHURCHES, AND I PROMISED THE CHRISTIANS IN EPHESUS I WOULD BE BACK...

ONCE AGAIN THE TIRELESS APOSTLE TOOK UP HIS PILGRIM STAFF: TARSUS, DERBE, LYSTRA, ICONIUM, ANTIOCH IN PISIDIA...

A YEAR LATER...

EPHESUS!

CRADLE OF PHILOSOPHY AND CITY OF ARTEMIS* MAY YOU OPEN YOUR HEART TO THE LOVE OF CHRIST!

* Goddess of fertility.

PAUL STAYED IN EPHESUS FOR THREE YEARS. WITH THE HELP OF MANY DISCIPLES, HE SPREAD THE GOOD NEWS.

IN THE NAME OF JESUS, BE HEALED!

JESUS HAS FULFILLED EVERYTHING THE PROPHETS FORETOLD!

I GIVE UP ALL MY MAGIC!

BE BAPTIZED, AND THE SPIRIT WILL LIVE IN YOUR HEARTS!

I'LL SOON BE LEAVING EPHESUS FOR MACEDONIA AND ACHAIA. TIMOTHY AND ERASTUS MUST GO ON AHEAD... THE TIME IS GETTING SHORT!

THE SUCCESS OF THE CHRISTIANS HAD UPSET SOME OF THE WORKING PEOPLE IN EPHESUS. ONE OF THEM WAS A SILVERSMITH NAMED DEMETRIUS...

THIS FELLOW PREACHES EVERYWHERE THAT OUR GODS AREN'T GODS AT ALL! NOW THERE ARE FAR FEWER PILGRIMS THIS YEAR...

...AND IF WE LET THIS GO ON, ONE OF THESE DAYS WE WON'T HAVE ANY WORK!

LET'S STIR UP THE CITY AGAINST HIM!

THE RIOT SPREAD THROUGHOUT THE CITY, AND EVERYBODY RUSHED TO THE THEATRE.

GREAT IS ARTEMIS OF EPHESUS!

THOSE TWO ARE COMPANIONS OF THE DECEIVER!

GLORY TO APOLLO!

KILL THEM!

THE CROWD WENT ON SHOUTING FOR SEVERAL HOURS. THEN THE TOWN CLERK STEPPED FORWARD.

CITIZENS OF EPHESUS! CALM DOWN! THESE MEN AREN'T GUILTY OF DISHONOURING ARTEMIS, OUR GREAT GODDESS! BUT, BECAUSE OF THIS UNLAWFUL GATHERING, WE RUN THE RISK THAT ROME WILL ACCUSE US OF A RIOT.

I ORDER YOU TO DISPERSE AND GO HOME!

THE RIOT MADE PAUL LEAVE EPHESUS ALL THE SOONER. SO HIS FRUITFUL STAY IN THE CITY ENDED. DURING THIS TIME, THE APOSTLE TO THE PAGANS HAD LAID THE FOUNDATION OF THE CHURCH IN EPHESUS, AND BY HIS LETTERS HAD ENCOURAGED THE CHRISTIANS IN CORINTH AND OTHER PLACES.

DURING THE SUMMER OF 57 PAUL VISITED THE CHURCHES IN PHILIPPI AND THESSALONICA. HE RETURNED TO CORINTH AT THE BEGINNING OF THE WINTER.

WE'VE NEEDED YOU BADLY TO BRING SOME ORDER BACK INTO THE CONGREGATION.

MY HEART IS SET ON TWO PLANS: TO GO TO JERUSALEM, AND THEN TO ROME... IF IT IS GOD'S WILL!

WRITE THIS: BROTHERS, I WANT YOU TO KNOW THAT MANY TIMES I'VE PLANNED TO VISIT YOU... BUT SO FAR I'VE BEEN PREVENTED FROM DOING SO...

... I MUST GO TO GREEKS AND BARBARIANS, TO THE WISE AS WELL AS THE IGNORANT. WHAT IS MORE, I'M VERY EAGER TO PREACH THE GOSPEL TO YOU IN ROME.

THE NEXT SPRING...

PAUL, I BEG YOU: DON'T TAKE THE SHIP TO CAESAREA! THERE ARE MANY JEWS THERE. SOMETHING WILL HAPPEN TO YOU.

VERY WELL! I'LL GO BY LAND. IF I'M NOT IN JERUSALEM BEFORE PASSOVER, I'LL BE THERE FOR PENTECOST!

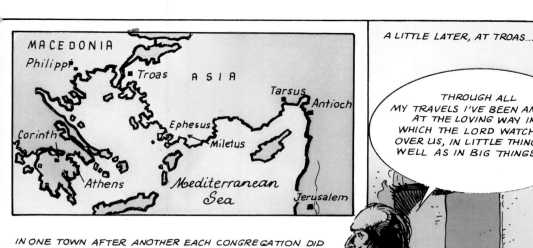

MACEDONIA
Philippi
Troas ASIA
Corinth
Ephesus
Miletus
Athens
Mediterranean Sea
Tarsus
Antioch
Jerusalem

IN ONE TOWN AFTER ANOTHER EACH CONGREGATION DID AS PAUL ASKED: IT CHOSE A BROTHER TO GO WITH HIM AND TAKE ITS OFFERING TO THE CHRISTIANS IN JERUSALEM.

A LITTLE LATER, AT TROAS...

THROUGH ALL MY TRAVELS I'VE BEEN AMAZED AT THE LOVING WAY IN WHICH THE LORD WATCHES OVER US, IN LITTLE THINGS AS WELL AS IN BIG THINGS...

SUDDENLY, WHILE PAUL WAS STILL PREACHING, A TEENAGER SITTING ON THE WINDOW-SILL FELL ASLEEP, AND...

EUTYCHUS!

HE'S DEAD!

LUKE BENT OVER THE BODY...

DON'T WORRY! HE'S STILL ALIVE!

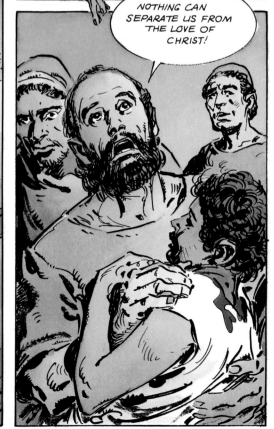

NOTHING CAN SEPARATE US FROM THE LOVE OF CHRIST!

PAUL AND HIS COMPANIONS LEFT TROAS AND SET SAIL FOR JERUSALEM. THEY STOPPED AT MILETUS.

THE ELDERS OF THE CHURCH IN EPHESUS HAVE JUST ARRIVED.

THAT IS FINE, LUKE! LET'S TALK TO THEM BY THEMSELVES.

I DON'T KNOW WHAT WILL HAPPEN TO ME IN JERUSALEM, BUT IN EVERY TOWN THE HOLY SPIRIT HAS WARNED ME THAT TROUBLE IS WAITING FOR ME.

I'VE PREACHED THE KINGDOM OF GOD TO YOU. NOW YOU'LL NEVER SEE ME AGAIN.

AFTER AGAIN ENCOURAGING THE BROTHERS, PAUL SAID GOODBYE TO THEM.

GOD PROTECT YOU, PAUL!

ONE DAY HE'LL BRING US TOGETHER AGAIN, AND WIPE AWAY ALL OUR TEARS.

AFTER LANDING ON COS, ON RHODES, AND AT TYRE, AT LAST PAUL ONCE AGAIN WALKED ON THE BLESSED SOIL OF HIS FATHERS AND HIS LORD.